# Ballet
## Show

Twist and spin with the ballerinas
as they get ready for their best show yet!

•

Use pens, pencils and stickers
to complete the activities on each page.

•

Where there is a missing sticker, you will see
an empty shape. Search your sticker pages
to find the missing sticker.

Don't forget to press out and create
dancing ballerinas and a sweet stage
from the card pages at the back of the book!

make
believe
ideas

# Dance-school dash

Use a pencil to trace the path to the dance school.

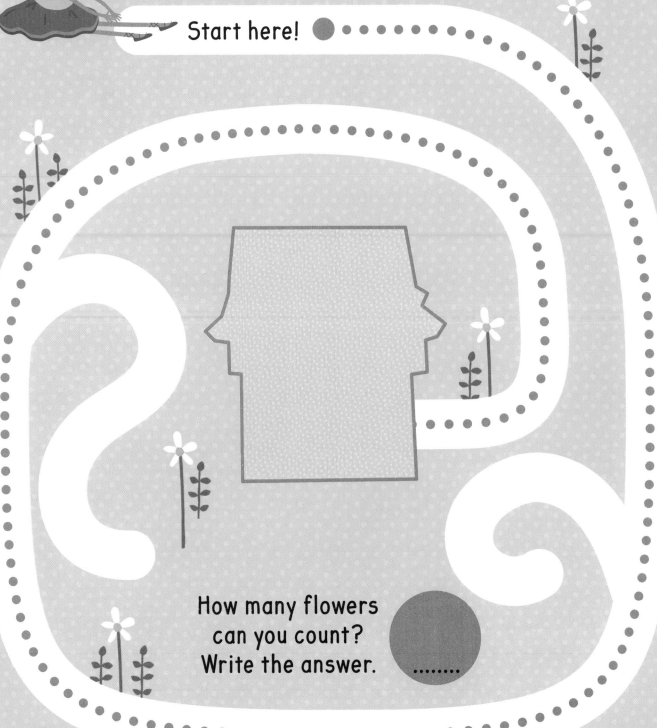

Start here!

How many flowers can you count? Write the answer. .........

# Award ceremony

Finish the ballerina's outfit.

Trace the trophy.

Colour the leotard.

Sticker the flowers.

# Busy backstage

Search the backstage scene for the things below.

1 ballerina

2 top hats

3 stars

Draw yourself in the mirror.

Colour the cat.

# Odd One Out

Circle the one that doesn't belong in each row.

# Dressing room

Find three differences between the scenes.

Sticker the star when you have finished and say, "I did it!"

# Colourful costumes

Colour the tutu blue.

Colour the shoes yellow.

Colour the bow green.

Sticker the pink ballet dress.

# Dance tour

Colour and sticker to finish
the ballerina tour.

BALLERINAS ON TOUR

Can you find the dog?
Trace the tick
when you've found him.

# Fairy forest

Count the things in the forest to finish the sums.

2 + 3 = ........

2 + 2 = ........

2 + 1 = ........

# Tricky trails

Trace the ballerina trails
with your finger.

Who is wearing orange?
Trace the tick
when you've found her.

# Ballet bags

Finish the kit in the ballet bags.

WATER

# Perfect pairs

Draw a line to match each dancer to their partner.

# Teatime

Trace the lines to finish the dancer's cups.
Then, sticker some tasty treats.

# Set the scene

Use colours to finish the set for the ballerina show!

How many ballerinas can you count? Write the answer.

.........

# Take a bow!

Finish the fairy costume using colour and stickers.

Can you count five roses? Trace the tick when you've found them.

# Beautiful ballerinas

Press out the ballerinas and shade the reverse sides. Then put your fingers through the holes to make the ballerinas dance!